INTRODUCTION

The goal of **EXPLORATIONS IN MUSIC, Books 1-7** is to expand the idea of music theory to points beyond the written page, to have your students realize that the music they are performing, listening to, and composing evolves from the realm of music theory.

I believe students can best understand how music is constructed by working with each musical idea in a number of different ways—writing, listening, analyzing scores, investigating their own repertoire, experimenting with composing, and various other creative activities. With this broad understanding, your students will make connections between the study of music theory and the music they hear, perform, and create.

Joanne Haroutounian
Arlington, Virginia

FEATURES OF EXPLORATIONS IN MUSIC, Books 1-7

· **Students explore and discover** new concepts.

· **Each concept** is used in a variety of ways, always including opportunities for creativity.

· **Creative experimentation** encourages students to compose.

· **Listening** examples are interwoven throughout the book and presented on a cassette tape. Students make the "eye and ear" connections with the score.

· **Cassette tape**s are provided with each book to allow listening to be done outside of lesson time—at home or in theory classes.

· **Explore** sections allow students to analyze the musical score with "eye and ear"and work creatively with musical ideas.

· **Explore Bonus** sections offer the curious student a challenge, providing motivation to work beyond what is already presented.

· **Beyond the Page** sections offer opportunities to link the student's current repertoire directly to the concepts developed in **EXPLORATIONS IN MUSIC.**

· A **Teacher's Guide** is correlated to each student book, providing many extra creative activities and the answers.

JOANNE HAROUTOUNIAN

Joanne Haroutounian has several special interests in music. She teaches piano students in her Arlington, Virginia, studio and engages them in many creative studio projects. She is also on the adjunct faculty of George Mason University. She has taught general music in the public schools and music education at the college level.

Joanne frequently performs chamber music with her husband, William, a violinist with the National Symphony. Her explorations into the area of arts education for gifted students led her to pursue a doctorate in educational psychology/gifted education at the University of Virginia.

She has presented numerous workshops on piano pedagogy, chamber music, special studio projects, and gifted education at local and state conventions as well as at the Music Teachers National Association, National Association for Gifted Children, and the National Conference on Piano Pedagogy.

Other publications by Mrs. Haroutounian are *Rhythm Antics* for elementary musicians, *Hummel's Concertino for Piano, op. 73* (two-piano score), and *Chamber Music Sampler, Books 1, 2, 3* for piano, violin, and cello. All books are published by the Neil A. Kjos Music Company.

WHAT WILL YOU DO?

 **WRITE**   Apply each new idea you learn through writing.

 **ANALYZE**   Discover details in the music by analyzing with your eyes and ears.

 **LISTEN**   Listen to the cassette tape to recognize new information in performed music and to develop skills through ear-training exercises. Each listening example is numbered in the book and announced on the tape.

 **INVESTIGATE**   Search for new ideas in this book and in the music you perform to discover specific information.

 **CREATE**   Experiment with your ideas by composing. Use your imagination to stretch your mind and your senses.

 **EXPLORE**   Learn to be curious! Research and expand on musical ideas.

Joanne Haroutounian

BOOK 2 CONTENTS

The **EXPLORATIONS IN MUSIC, Book 2** cassette includes listening examples for each time you see the symbol 🎵.
The compilation of the following excerpts is provided by PolyGram Special Markets, a division of PolyGram Group Distribution, Inc. (P) 1993:
Wolfgang Amadeus Mozart: *Menuetto from Clarinet Quintet in A Major K.581,* Members of the Wiener Oktett
Johann Sebastian Bach: *Vivace from Concerto for Two Violins, Strings and Continuo in D Minor BWV 1043,* Violinists Zino Francescatti and Reis
  Fasquier with Festival Strings Lucerne, Rudolph Baumgartner, Conductor
Wolfgang Amadeus Mozart: *Andante from Symphony No. 31 K.297 ("Paris")* Royal Concertgebouw Orchestra, Amsterdam, Josef Krips, Conductor
Joseph Haydn: *Allegro moderato from String Quartet in D Major, op. 64 no. 5 Hob:III:63 ("The Lark")* Amadeus Quartet

WP351	ISBN 0-8497-9532-X	book and casette
WP351B	ISBN 0-8497-9566-4	book only

©1993 Neil A. Kjos Music Company, 4380 Jutland Drive, San Diego, California 92117.
International copyright secured. All rights reserved. Printed in U.S.A.

THE STARTING POINT: A REVIEW

1. Draw a **treble clef** on the staff below. Draw notes around the dots and identify by letter name.

2. Draw a **bass clef** on the staff below. Draw notes around the dots and identify by letter name.

3. The letter names of the **lines** of the **treble staff** are ____ ____ ____ ____ ____

4. The letter names of the **spaces** of the **treble staff** are ____ ____ ____ ____

5. The letter names of the **lines** of the **bass staff** are ____ ____ ____ ____ ____

6. The letter names of the **spaces** of the **bass staff** are ____ ____ ____ ____

7. Draw **bar lines** and a **double bar** correctly, observing the **time signature** and **writing the counts** below each measure.

Counts:_____

8. Write the **counts** below each measure. Write the **time signature** you discover in the box.

Counts:_____

9. Draw a **melody shape** going **up** by **steps**.

10. Draw a **melody shape** going **up and down** by **skips**.

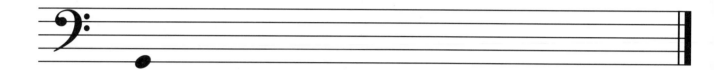

11. Write the correct number of beats in $\frac{3}{4}$ or $\frac{4}{4}$ for each note or rest.

_____   _____   _____   _____   _____

12. Draw the following Major **triads**.

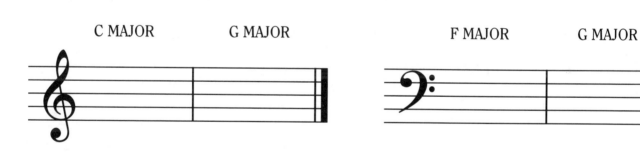

13. Match the words to the correct definitions.

A. forte   _f_   _____ soft

B. crescendo   ⟨   _____ on the staff that has high notes

C. treble clef   𝄞   _____ gradually getting softer

D. piano   _p_   _____ loud

E. decrescendo   ⟩   _____ gradually getting louder

F. bass clef   𝄢   _____ on the staff that has low notes

THE GRAND STAFF

The **GRAND STAFF** is the music "paper" on which music is written. Look carefully to see how to draw the staff correctly with **BAR and BRACE**, **TREBLE CLEF**, **BASS CLEF**, and **DOUBLE BAR.** Within the staff, music is divided into **MEASURES** by using **BAR LINES.**

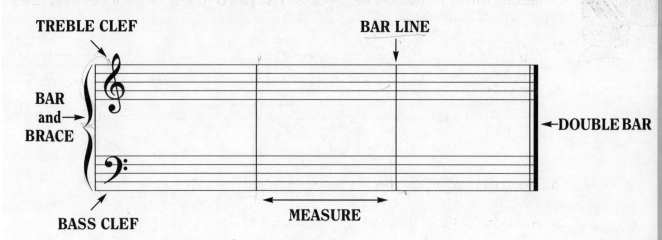

It is important to draw the **TREBLE CLEF** exactly around the **second line from the BOTTOM** of the treble staff.

It is important to draw the **BASS CLEF** exactly around the **second line from the TOP** of the bass staff.

1. Practice drawing several **treble clefs** and **bass clefs**.

2. Label each part of the empty **grand staff** to match the staff pictured at the top of the page.

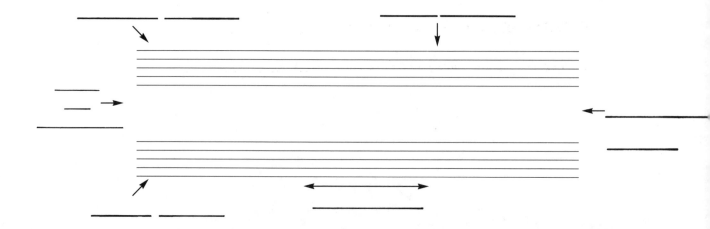

The letter names for the **treble staff** and the **bass staff** follow the music alphabet from the bottom of the staff to the top.

Notes written on the treble staff are written in the **TREBLE CLEF**.

Notes written on the bass staff are written in the **BASS CLEF**.

3. Review what you have learned about the letter names of the **treble clef** and **bass clef** by writing in the missing letters. If you need help, look at **FACTS TO KNOW** on the inside front cover music

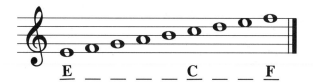

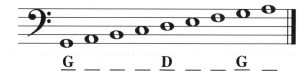

E _ _ _ _ C _ _ F   G _ _ _ D _ _ G _

4. The **grand staff** below contains notes written on both lines and spaces.

A. Color all of the notes that are on **lines red.** ──O──

B. Color all of the notes that are on **spaces blue.** ◯

C. Identify all of the notes on the staff by **letter** name.

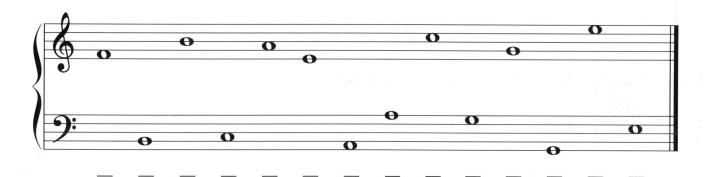

_ _ _ _ _ _ _ _ _ _ _ _

5. Discover the words you have colored by writing the letter names asked for.

A. Treble clef line notes you colored are ____ ____ ____

B. Bass clef line notes you colored are ____ ____ ____

C. Treble clef space notes you colored are ____ ____ ____ ____

D. Bass clef space notes you colored are ____ ____ ____ ____

LESSON 2 — LETTER NAMES ON THE GRAND STAFF

You have learned to draw notes in the **treble clef** and **bass clef** separately.
Now you can combine both into the **GRAND STAFF**.

1. Draw all of the **line** notes of the **grand staff** from bottom to top. Identify by letter name.

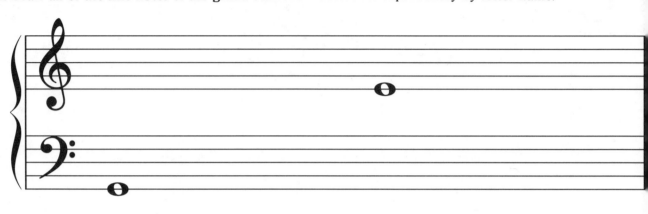

2. Draw all of the **space** notes of the **grand staff** from bottom to top. Identify by letter name.

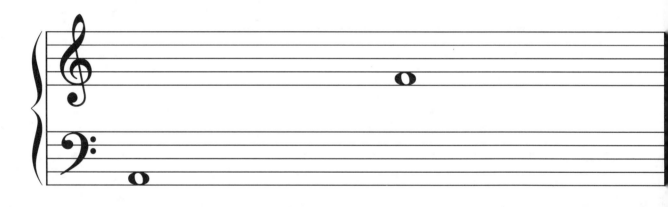

3. You learned about **Middle C** in **EXPLORATIONS IN MUSIC, Book 1**. It is written in the **middle** of the grand staff and it is located at the middle of the piano keyboard.

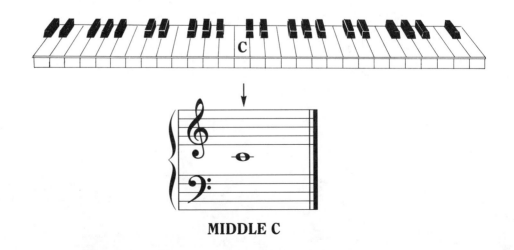

MIDDLE C

4. The notes shown on the grand staff below are located **next to Middle C** and between the treble clef and bass clef. Discover the letter names of these new notes by writing the music alphabet around them.

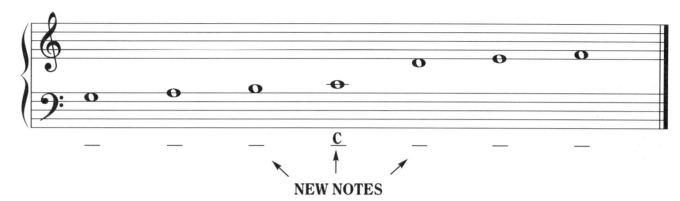

NEW NOTES

5. Write the letter names of the notes. They include the new notes and spell words.

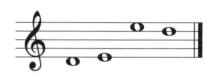  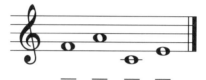

6. Draw notes to match the letter names. Try to use at least one of the notes you learned on this page in each "music word."

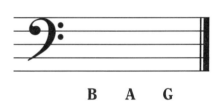  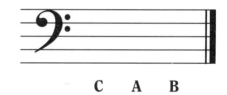

B A G   **D A D**   **C A B**

EXPLORE Draw **all** of the notes on the grand staff that match the letter names. Remember the notes **between** the staffs!

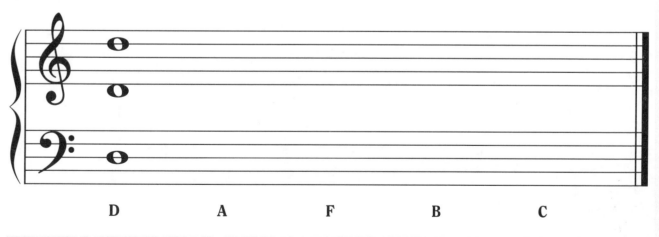

D   A   F   B   C

PRACTICE PAGE

1. Prepare a **grand staff** with **treble** and **bass clefs, bar and brace**, a **measure** separated by two **bar lines**, and a **double bar**.

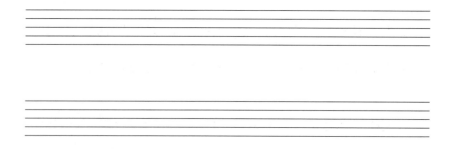

2. Write the **letter names** of the notes on the grand staff. They should spell words.

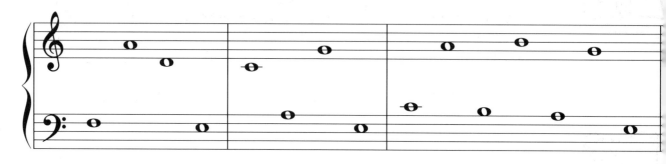

3. Draw **all** the notes on the grand staff for the letters indicated.

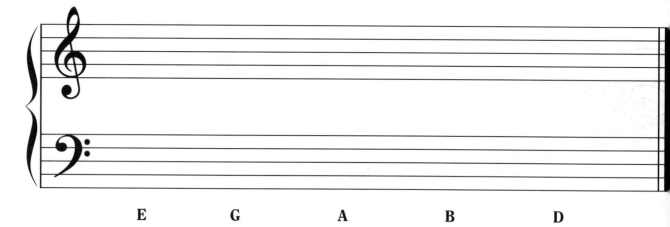

E   G   A   B   D

EXPLORE Create your own "music words." Remember, words must use only the letters A B C D E F G.

EXPLORE

To learn the letter names of the line and space notes on the staff easily, you can make up simple sentences using the letter names as the first letter of the words in the sentence.

TREBLE CLEF LINES   Every Good Boy Does Fine

BASS CLEF LINES   Good Boys Do Fine Always

1. Use your **imagination** and **create your own sentences** to help you remember the lines and spaces!

Treble clef lines: E_____ G_____ B_____ D_____ F_____

Treble clef spaces: F   A   C   E. This one is easy because it spells a word.

Bass clef lines: G_____ B_____ D_____ F_____ A_____

Bass clef spaces: A _____ C_____ E_____ G_____

2. Draw a treble clef on the staff.

The **treble clef** is often called a **G CLEF.** Remembering how you drew the treble clef, can you discover **why** it is called a G clef?

It is called a **G clef** because_____

3. Draw a bass clef on the staff.

The **bass clef** is often called an **F CLEF.** Remembering how you drew the bass clef, can you discover **why** it is called an F clef?

It is called an **F clef** because_____

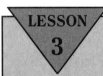

LESSON 3

MUSIC STORIES

The story below uses "music words" written on the grand staff.

 1. Write the letter names of the "music words" in the following story.

THE VACATION

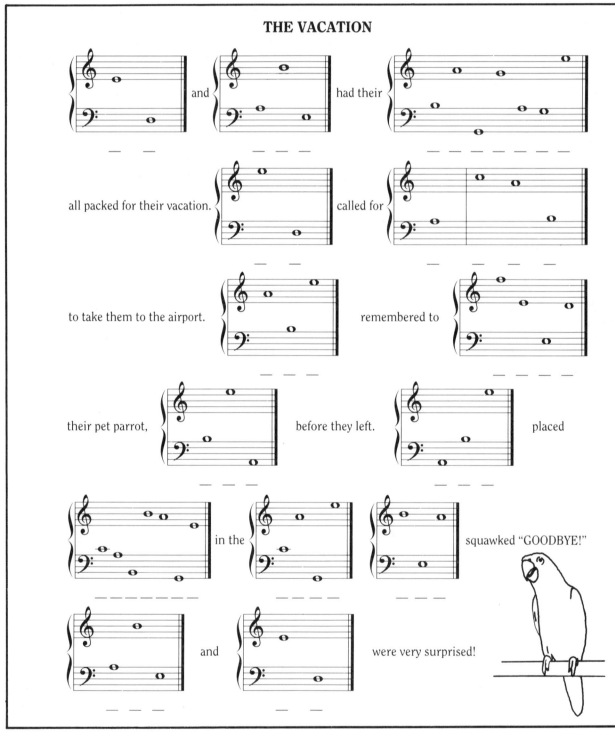

2. Now it is your turn to create your own **music story.** First, find as many words as you can using only the letters A B C D E F G. Write them below.

3. Use your imagination and use the words from the list in number 2 in a story. <u>Underline</u> the music words.

_____

_____

_____

_____

4. Write your music story below, using the staff paper to write the notes on the staff that spell your music words. Draw blanks to fill in letter names under each note. Let your friends try to fill in the letter names of **your** musical story!

Title: _____

Written by: _____ **Date:** _____

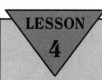

RHYTHM REVIEW

LESSON 4

EXPLORATIONS IN MUSIC, Book 1 presented the following notes and rest in rhythm:

SYLLABLES to help you clap and "bob"(⌢ = "bob") to the beat.

QUARTER NOTE	♩ = 1 BEAT	You say:	ta
		You:	clap
HALF NOTE	♩ = 2 BEATS	You say:	half-note
		You:	clap-bob
DOTTED HALF NOTE	♩. = 3 BEATS	You say:	half-note-dot
		You:	clap-bob-bob
WHOLE NOTE	𝅝 = 4 BEATS	You say:	Hold-that-whole -note
		You:	clap-bob-bob-bob
QUARTER REST	𝄽 = 1 BEAT	You whisper:	"rest"
		You:	open hands

The **EXPLORATIONS** tape is used whenever you see the symbol.

1. The rhythms below use **syllables and words**. Try these exercises two different ways:
   - Clap as you say the syllables and words out loud.
   - Clap and "think" the syllables and words in your head.

Check your work with the **EXPLORATIONS** tape.

A.

ta   ta   half - note   half - note   half - note   ta   ta   "rest"   ta   hold - that - whole - note

B.

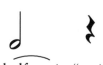

half - note - dot   ta   ta   ta   half - note   "rest"   ta   "rest"   ta   half - note - dot

2. The rhythms below use **counts**. Try these exercises two different ways:
  · Clap while you count out loud.
  · Clap and "think" the counts in your head.

Check your work with the **EXPLORATIONS** tape.

A.

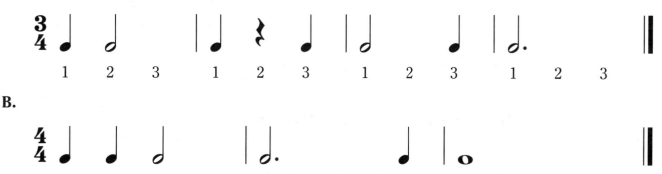

B.

3. Which way was more comfortable for you?   SYLLABLES   COUNTING

4. Use whichever way was the most comfortable in doing these **more challenging** rhythms.
   Check your work with the **EXPLORATIONS** tape.

A.

B.

C.

5. Your turn! Write a challenging rhythm using ♩ ♩ ♩. 𝅝 𝄽

EXPLORE For extra fun, perform the rhythms above with the following motions.

PAT LEGS	TOUCH TOES	TOUCH NOSE	ARMS OUT	STRETCH HIGH

LESSON 5

TIME SIGNATURES

EXPLORATIONS IN MUSIC, Book 1 introduced the following **TIME SIGNATURES**:

3 3 BEATS IN EACH MEASURE
4 QUARTER NOTE ♩ = 1 beat

4 4 BEATS IN EACH MEASURE
4 QUARTER NOTE ♩ = 1 beat

The TOP number tells how many beats are in each measure.
The BOTTOM number tells what kind of note = 1 beat.

4 = QUARTER NOTE   2 = HALF NOTE

Each measure below contains the correct amount of beats to match the time signature at the beginning of the staff. "Counts" are written for each beat in the measures.

Each measure has:

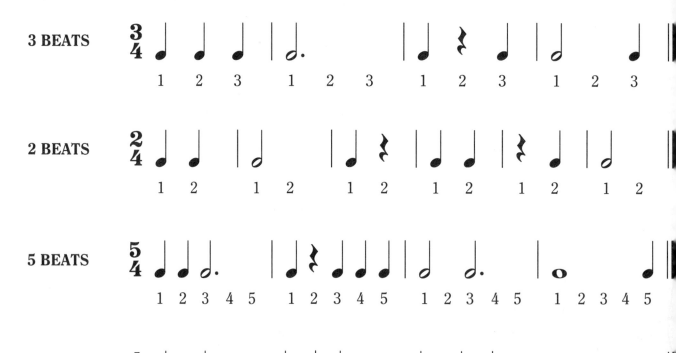

3 BEATS

2 BEATS

5 BEATS

4 BEATS

EXPLORE Look for clues on this page to discover what this time signature means.

2 _____
2 _____ = 1 BEAT

1. The measures below are missing notes or rests. **Fill each measure** with the correct number of beats, matching the **top** number of the **time signature.**

A.

$\frac{3}{4}$ ♩　♩　｜♩　｜♩　｜

　　1　2　3　　1　2　3　　1　2　3　　1　2　3

B.

$\frac{2}{4}$ ♩　｜♩　｜　｜♩　｜♩　｜　｜

　　1　2　　1　2　　1　2　　1　2　　1　2　　1　2

C.

$\frac{5}{4}$ ♩　♩　｜𝅝　｜♩.　｜

　　1　2　3　4　5　　1　2　3　4　5　　1　2　3　4　5

2. Now it is **your** turn to **write the correct counts** below each measure.

A.

$\frac{4}{4}$ ♩　♩　♩　｜♩　♩　♩　｜♩.　♩　｜𝅝　｜

Counts:_____

B.

$\frac{2}{4}$ ♩　｜♩　♩　｜♩　｜♩　♩　｜♩　♩　｜♩　｜

Counts:_____

3. Fill the empty measures below to match the **time signatures**. **Write the counts** below each measure to check that you are correct.

A.

$\frac{2}{4}$ ｜　｜　｜　｜　｜　｜

Counts:_____

B.

$\frac{3}{4}$ ｜　｜　｜　｜　｜

Counts:_____

C.

$\frac{5}{4}$ ｜　｜　｜

Counts: _____

RHYTHM WORKOUT

This **RHYTHM WORKOUT** includes measures with 2, 3, 4, and 5 beats. Follow the directions using the metronome at the indicated markings.

EASY GOING = 80   MEDIUM CHALLENGE = 92   SUPER CHALLENGE = 100

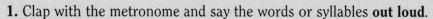

1. Clap with the metronome and say the words or syllables **out loud**.
2. Clap with the metronome and "think" the words or syllables.
3. Keep a steady beat "inside" with no metronome and "think" the words or syllables while clapping the rhythms.
4. **Step the steady beat** while clapping and listening to the rhythms on the **EXPLORATIONS** tape–a final check to your workout!

A.

B.

C.

D.

E. Your rhythm! You can choose how many beats you want in each measure

RATE YOUR WORKOUT: I reached the level of _____ on the metronome.
My rating is: ☐ SUPER JOB!   ☐ DOING O.K.   ☐ NEEDS MORE WORK

1. Try the challenge of **clapping** and **stamping** to the rhythm exercise below.

2. Now it is **your** turn to write a **two-line rhythm**. Remember to have **4 beats** in each measure.

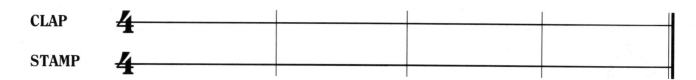

3. The three-line staff below includes **patschen**—tapping your legs with your hands. Remember to have **2 beats** in each measure.

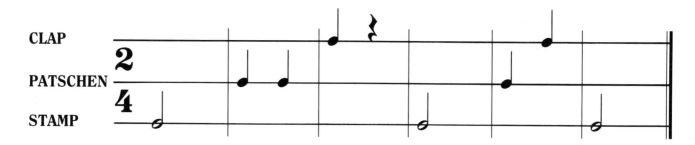

4. Your turn again! Write a three-line rhythm exercise with **2 beats** in each measure.

CLAP

PATSCHEN

STAMP

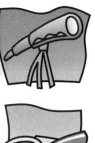

EXPLORE Another Rhythm Challenge! Combine exercises 1 and 2 with two groups performing together. Then combine exercises 3 and 4. What happens when you have **all four** exercises performed at once?

LESSON 6

RESTS

RESTS are used in music to show silence—**no** clapping or playing.

QUARTER REST	HALF REST	WHOLE REST
= 1 BEAT	= 2 BEATS	= 4 BEATS

It is important to write the rests correctly on the staff. It is easy to get the **HALF REST** and **WHOLE REST** mixed up because they look similar.

The **half rest** is written **ABOVE the middle line** of the staff.
It "sits" on top of the line.

The **whole rest** is written **BELOW the fourth line from the bottom** of the staff.
It "holds on" to the line.

1. Practice writing half rests and whole rests.

HALF RESTS

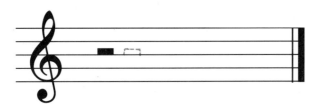

WHOLE RESTS

2. Practice writing quarter rests.

QUARTER REST

NOTES AND RESTS IN RHYTHMS

When using rests in rhythm exercises, **whisper** the word **"rest"** for each beat of rest as you **bob hands open to show each beat of rest**. For the whole rest say "rest-rest-whole-rest" to show 4 beats of rest.

3. With the **EXPLORATIONS** tape, clap the rhythms, say the syllables and words, and whisper the "rests."

A.

| 1 | 2 | 3 — 4 | 1 | 2 | 3 | 4 | 1 | 2 | 3 | 4 | 1 | 2 | 3 | 4 |
| ta | ta | half - note | ta | "rest" | half - note | | "rest - rest" | ta | ta | | hold - that - whole - note |

B.

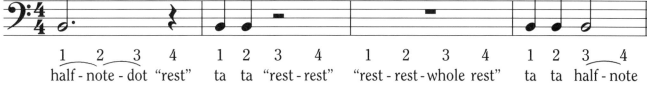

| 1 | 2 | 3 | 4 | 1 | 2 | 3 | 4 | 1 | 2 | 3 | 4 | 1 | 2 | 3 | 4 |
| half - note - dot | "rest" | ta | ta | "rest - rest" | | "rest - rest - whole rest" | | | ta | ta | half - note |

4. Draw bar lines and double bars in the correct places. Look carefully at the time signatures and **write the counts** below each measure.

A.

Counts: _____

B.

Counts: _____

C.

Counts: _____

5. Complete each measure with one **rest. Write the counts** below each measure to check your work.

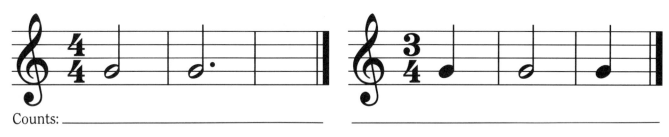

Counts: _____

PRACTICE PAGE

You can have fun solving some problems on this practice page. Each example needs **your** help!

1. Where did the **time signatures** go? Please **write the counts below each measure** to find out how many beats are in each measure. Then **write the time signatures** in the boxes to solve our first problem.

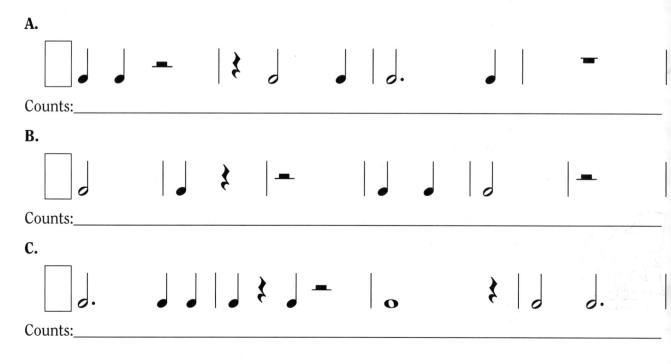

A.

Counts:_____

B.

Counts:_____

C.

Counts:_____

2. Where did the **bar lines** and **double bar** go? Look carefully at the **time signature. Write the counts** below each measure to match these time signatures. **Draw bar lines** as you discover each full measure and **end with a double bar**.

A.

Counts:_____

B.

Counts:_____

C.

Counts:_____

3. More problems! The measures below are missing notes and rests. We need your help to **complete each measure** to match the correct number of beats with notes or rests.

A.

B.

C.

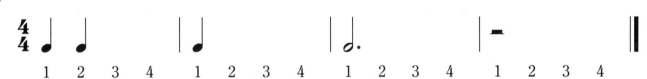

4. Oh no! Empty measures! Your job is to **fill them correctly with notes and rests** you have learned and **write the counts** below each measure. Thank you!

A.

Counts:_____

B.

Counts:_____

C.

Counts:_____

EXPLORE A rhythm **OSTINATO** is a rhythm pattern that is repeated continuously through a composition. Combine the rhythm ostinato below with the rhythm you created in number 4 A by "performing" with a friend. Create your own **ostinatos** for 4 B and 4 C.

4A **4B** **4C**

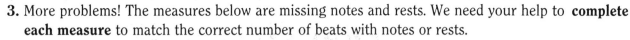

WP351

LISTEN, AND CREATE RHYTHMS

You are now ready to identify rhythms by listening like a **Musical Detective**!

1. Clap the rhythm exercises below and use the syllables and words to help you keep the beat even. You may want to write the counts below each measure.

2. Clap the rhythm exercises again and keep the words "in your head." Listen to your careful clapping with the even beat.

3. Listen to the **EXPLORATIONS** tape. Three of the rhythm examples are played on the tape. After listening carefully, write the letter names of the examples you heard.

1. Do you hear A or B? _____

A.

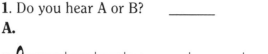

B.

2. Do you hear C or D? _____

C.

D.

3. Do you hear E or F? _____

E.

F.

Rhythms have a natural **ACCENT**, a **stronger beat,** on the first beat of each measure.
The measures below show this **accent** with a sign > , though normally this is "felt" and played without a sign.

4. Listen to the following rhythm examples on the **EXPLORATIONS** tape:

A.

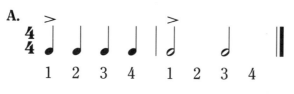

C.

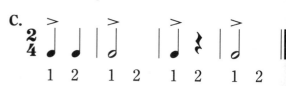

B.

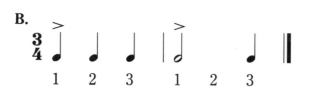

D.

5. Listen to the examples on the **EXPLORATIONS** tape in $\frac{2}{4}$ $\frac{3}{4}$ or $\frac{4}{4}$ Circle what you hear.

A. $\frac{2}{4}$ $\frac{3}{4}$ $\frac{4}{4}$ **C.** $\frac{2}{4}$ $\frac{3}{4}$ $\frac{4}{4}$

B. $\frac{2}{4}$ $\frac{3}{4}$ $\frac{4}{4}$ **D.** $\frac{2}{4}$ $\frac{3}{4}$ $\frac{4}{4}$

A RHYTHM INVENTION

You can create rhythm exercises in many ways—using words, different movements, and combining rhythms. Why not try **all** of these ways in the following **rhythm invention**!

1. Find words to fit a rhythm you have created.

Example: Rhythm

Words: See that sil - ly   ghost   there!   BOO!   I   must   hide!

Your rhythm: $\frac{4}{4}$

Your words:_____

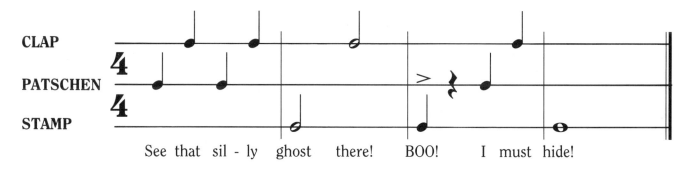

2. Copy this rhythm on the following three-line rhythm staff. (You can touch your head on the 𝄽.)

CLAP	
PATSCHEN	
STAMP	

See that sil - ly   ghost   there!   BOO!   I   must   hide!

CLAP	
PATSCHEN	
STAMP	

Your words: _____

3. "Perform" the rhythm exercise while saying the words out loud.

EXPLORE Would you like a "Two-Part Rhythm Invention"? Have two people or groups perform both "inventions" above **at the same time**, whispering the words.

EXPLORE

You can now learn to investigate a page of music like a **Musical Detective**!

A Sad Tale, p. 39 no. 16 by Dmitri Kabalevsky (opening 8 measures)

Time to investigate! Look carefully at the music above to discover the answers below.

1. What is the **time signature** of the piece?

2. What is the letter name of the first note in the **treble clef**? _____

3. What is the letter name of the first note in the **bass clef**? _____

4. Look at this rhythm pattern:
   Notes are often written "upside down" to fit onto the staff.

   Can you find this **rhythm pattern** in the music? **Circle** the pattern each time you see it. This pattern was used _____ times in the music.

Now listen to the music of Kabalevsky's *A Sad Tale* on the **EXPLORATIONS** tape and answer these questions.

6. **Dynamics** are markings in music that color the sounds you hear. Was the music you heard **loud** or **soft**? _____

Look carefully at the music for the letters *p* and *pp*. Investigate the Music Dictionary on page 55 to find the meaning of the music symbols.

p = _____   *pp* = _____

7. A **melody** is what you would sing in music—the tune of the music. Listen to the tape one more time and decide which clef (treble or bass) plays the melody of the music.

The **melody** is played in the _____ clef.

EXPLORE Write other new ideas you found in the music. Investigate with your teacher to solve these musical "clues."

_____

BEYOND THE PAGE

You have learned to look for details in rhythms, note letter names, and dynamics. Investigating the music you learn at lessons for these same details will take the ideas beyond the page of this book into your own music. Enjoy writing this report that fills in the details about a favorite piece of yours!

Music Investigation Report

Title _____

Composer _____ **Date of report**_____

1. What is the **time signature?**

2. What are the letter names of the **first and last notes?** (Include both treble and bass notes if you play a keyboard instrument.)

The first note(s) is (are): 𝄞 _____ 𝄢 ___ . The last note(s) is (are): 𝄞 _____ 𝄢 ___

3. Locate **repeated rhythm patterns.** Draw the pattern and write the measure numbers where you found this pattern.

Repeated rhythm pattern(s)   Found in measures:

_____   _____

_____   _____

4. At the beginning of the piece, which clef has the **melody?** _____

5. Create a dynamic **"color path"** for one page of the piece by writing the dynamics in the order in which they appear.

Example: *p* ⤙ *mf* ⤙ *ff*   *mp* ⤚ *pp*

The **dynamic color path** for page _____ looks like this:

Congratulations! You have learned how to be a Music Detective in your own music!

PRACTICE PAGE

 Use the space below for extra rhythm exercises, note letter name drills, and music stories.

UNIT 1

TEST

TEST YOUR SKILLS

1. Draw the **grand staff** below with **brace and bar**, **treble clef**, **bass clef**, and **double bar**. Draw **two bar lines** to make measures.

_____ *of 4 points*

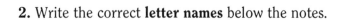

2. Write the correct **letter names** below the notes.

_____ *of 12 points*

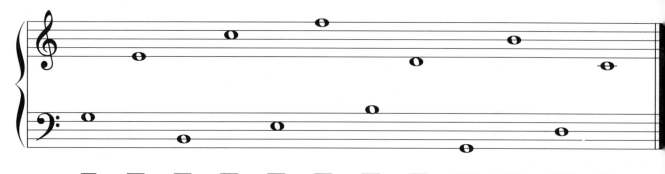

3. Draw **all** of the notes indicated on the **grand staff**.

_____ *of 10 points*

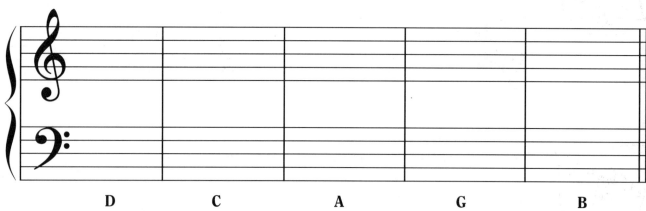

D   C   A   G   B

4. **Draw bar lines and double bars** in the correct places. Look carefully at the time signatures.
Write the counts under each measure.

_____ *of 36 points*

A.

Counts:_____

B.

C.

Counts:_____

D.

5. Complete each measure with **one note. Write the counts** below each measure. _____ *of 14 points*

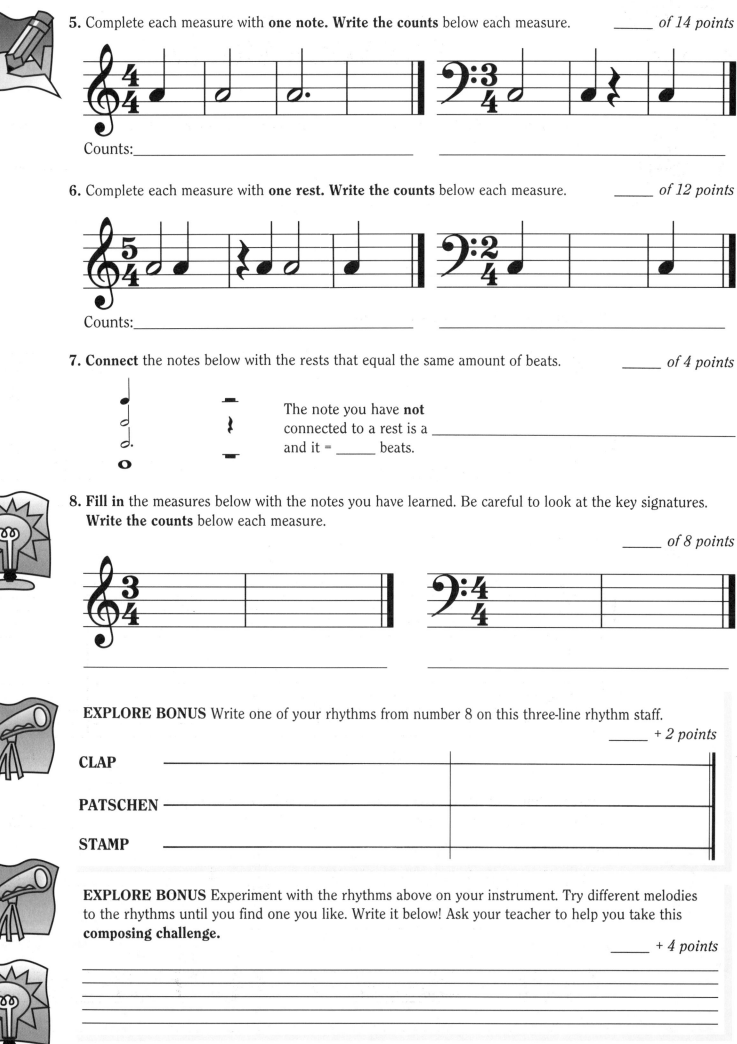

Counts:_____   _____

6. Complete each measure with **one rest. Write the counts** below each measure. _____ *of 12 points*

Counts:_____   _____

7. Connect the notes below with the rests that equal the same amount of beats. _____ *of 4 points*

The note you have **not**
connected to a rest is a _____
and it = _____ beats.

8. Fill in the measures below with the notes you have learned. Be careful to look at the key signatures.
Write the counts below each measure.

_____ *of 8 points*

EXPLORE BONUS Write one of your rhythms from number 8 on this three-line rhythm staff.

_____ *+ 2 points*

CLAP

PATSCHEN

STAMP

EXPLORE BONUS Experiment with the rhythms above on your instrument. Try different melodies
to the rhythms until you find one you like. Write it below! Ask your teacher to help you take this
composing challenge.

_____ *+ 4 points*

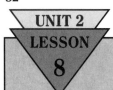

INTERVALS

The distance between two notes is called an **INTERVAL.** To discover the number names of intervals, think of the first note as **"1"** and count from there.

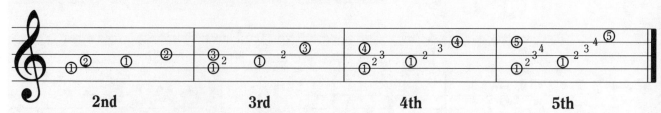

Intervals can be written two different ways:
- as a **MELODY**, with one note following the other
- as a **HARMONY**, with both notes sounding together

EACH INTERVAL AS A MELODY

EACH INTERVAL AS A HARMONY

Look carefully at the intervals on this page and write the interval number that fits the sentence. Some will require more than one interval as an answer.

1. When the bottom note is a space, the top note is a space.   _____ _____

2. When the bottom note is a space, the top note is a line.   _____ _____

3. When written as a harmony, the notes are side-by-side, touching.   _____

4. When the bottom note is a line, the top note is the next line up.   _____

5. This interval could be called a skip because it skips one note.   _____

6. This interval could be called the head and bottom of a musical "snowman" with the middle missing—a double skip.   _____

7. This interval could be called a step.   _____

EXPLORE Play the intervals from this page on your instrument over and over. If your instrument can play them as harmonies also, experiment with those sounds as well. In your own words, describe what the following intervals sound like.

2nds sound like: _____

5ths sound like: _____

8. Identify the following intervals by putting a **2, 3, 4, or 5** on the blanks.

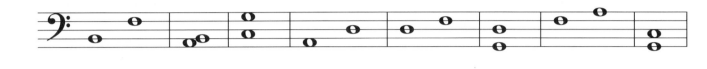

9. Circle **all** the intervals above that are written as **melodies.** How many? _____

10. Draw the indicated intervals above the notes as **harmonies.**

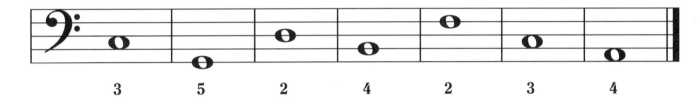

11. Draw the indicated intervals above the notes as **melodies.**

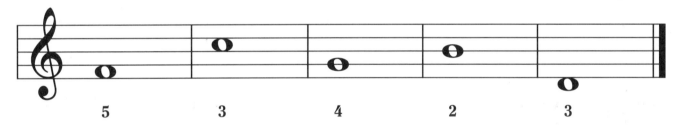

EXPLORE Investigate the music below to find an interval that is used over and over. Listen to this example on the **EXPLORATIONS** tape and answer the questions below.

Playtime by Bela Bartok (measures 19-26)

The interval that is repeated often is the interval of a _____.

EXPLORE BONUS Write the letter names of the notes in the circled intervals.

1. ____ and _____   2. ____ and ____   3. ____ and ____

LESSON 9

LISTEN, AND CREATE MELODIES

1. The melody shapes you see below move up and down the staff by **steps (2nds)**. Listen to the melody shapes on the **EXPLORATIONS** tape. Put your pencil point on the first note and **trace the melody shape as you listen.**

A.

B.

2. These melody shapes move up and down the staff by **skips** or **3rds**. **Trace the melody shape** with your pencil point as you listen to the tape.

A.

B.

3. Melody **A** moves up and down by **steps (2nds)**. Melody **B** moves up and down by **skips (3rds)**. **Rhythm** has been added to the melody shape. **Trace the melody while you count the rhythm** "in your head" and listen to the tape.

A.
STEPS (2nds)

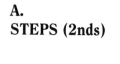 

B.
SKIPS (3rds)

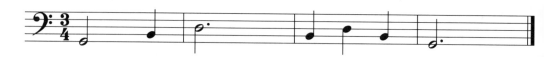

4. These melodies use both **steps (2nds)** and **skips (3rds)** with rhythms. **Trace the melody** and listen carefully for differences in the sounds of 2nds and 3rds.

A.
STEPS & SKIPS

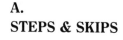 

B.
STEPS & SKIPS

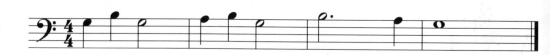

5. You have another opportunity to be a listening **Musical Detective**! Listen to discover melodies! The tape will play three of the melodies written below. **Before starting the tape, please read these directions.**

• **Before** listening, **trace each melody** with your pencil point **while singing** out loud or "in your head" and concentrate on steps, skips, and rhythms.

• **Do not trace any melody when listening to the tape.** Try to capture the melody "in your head" as you hear it played.

• **Sing the melody you hear** out loud or "in your head" and match it to a written melody.

You may repeat the taped examples if you need more listening time.

1. Do you hear A or B? _____

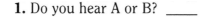

A.   B.

2. Do you hear C or D? _____

C.   D.

3. Do you hear E or F? _____

E.   F.

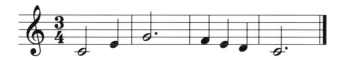

Bravo! Excellent listening! Now turn the page to create **your own** melodies.

EXPLORE Complete the following sentences after an "eye" analysis of the melodies above.

1. The melodies that begin with a skip are _____ _____ _____.

2. The melodies that begin with a step are _____ _____ _____.

EXPLORE BONUS Sing the **first three notes** of these familiar melodies "in your head" and circle what you hear.

Three Blind Mice:	STEPS	SKIPS	moving	UP	DOWN	UP & DOWN
The Star Spangled Banner:	STEPS	SKIPS	moving	UP	DOWN	UP & DOWN

CREATING MELODIES

- Experiment with a melody on your instrument using **steps** (2nds) and **skips** (3rds). Keep it short and simple.

- When you find a melody you like, write the **open noteheads** on the workspace below.

- Add a **time signature** and **rhythm** that fit well with your melody. Adjust bar lines and double bar to complete the melody on the staff.

- Share the melody with your teacher. Expand ideas until you have a full **COMPOSITION**!

COMPOSING WORKSPACE

PRACTICE PAGE

1. Write the indicated intervals above the notes as **harmonies**.

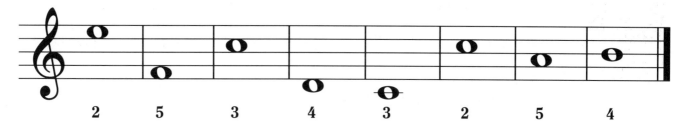

2. Identify the following intervals by **number**.

3. Circle each interval above that is written as a **melody**. How many? _____

4. Write the intervals above the notes as **melodies.**

5. Your turn to create a melody shape using only **2nds** up and down! The first note is written. Use only noteheads with no rhythm. Hear the melody "in your head" as you write.

6. Use the melody shape from number 5 and add a time signature and rhythm to complete your melody. Hear the melody and rhythm "inside" as you write.

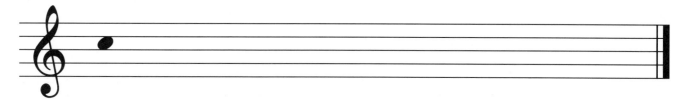

EXPLORE Play the melody you have created on your instrument. Make any changes that you would like, using only **2nds**.

HALF AND WHOLE STEPS

The easiest way to understand **HALF AND WHOLE STEPS** is to see them on a keyboard.
Notice the keyboard is made up of white and black keys.

When you move up or down to the very next note (white or black on the keyboard) by step and there
is **NO NOTE BETWEEN THE STEP**, it is a **HALF STEP**.

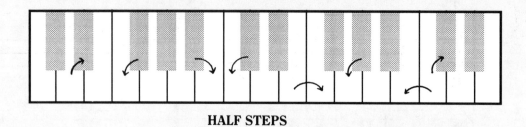

HALF STEPS

When you move up or down by **WHOLE STEP** there is a **NOTE IN THE MIDDLE OF THE STEP**.
Two half steps equal a whole step.

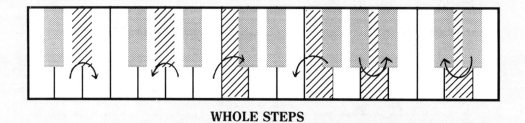

WHOLE STEPS

SHARPS AND FLATS

SHARPS When there is a ♯ before a note, the note is **RAISED** a half step.

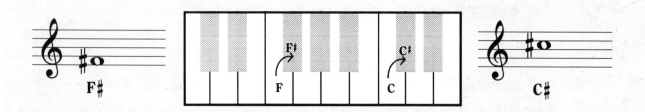

FLATS When there is a ♭ before a note, the note is **LOWERED** a half step.

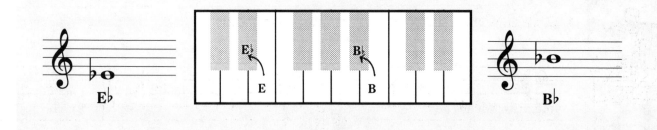

When writing **sharps** and **flats** on the staff, write them **before** the note **on the line or space of the note** they describe.

CORRECT **INCORRECT**

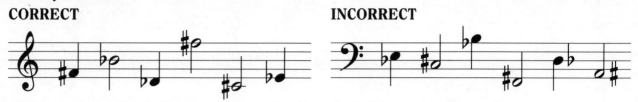

1. Write **sharps** before these notes. Write the note letter names on the blanks.

___ ___ ___ ___ ___ ___ ___

2. Write **flats** before these notes. Write the note letter names on the blanks .

___ ___ ___ ___ ___ ___ ___

NATURAL SIGN

A **NATURAL** sign cancels the ♯ or ♭ sign describing a note.

All of the signs you have learned – ♯ ♭ ♮ – are called **ACCIDENTALS.**

3. Write **naturals** before the notes. Write the note letter names on the blanks.

___ ___ ___ ___ ___ ___ ___

4. Circle all of the **accidentals** that are written **incorrectly**.

PENTACHORDS

A good way to understand the pattern of steps within a scale is to learn about **PENTACHORDS**– the first five notes of a scale.

A MAJOR PENTACHORD has a **whole step, whole step, half step, whole step** pattern.

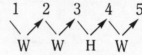

5 NOTES OF PENTACHORD   1 2 3 4 5

STEPS BETWEEN NOTES   W W H W

(W= Whole Step; H= Half Step)

Look at several Major **PENTACHORD PATTERNS**–

ON THE KEYBOARD   ⌒ = HALF STEP   **ON THE STAFF**

STARTING ON C

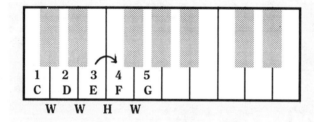

STARTING ON D

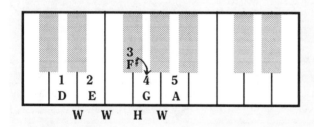

STARTING ON F

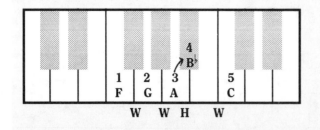

Now it is your turn to write pentachords on the staff and on the keyboard!

1. Draw the pentachord notes shown on each keyboard on the staffs. The first note is written. Remember ♯ and ♭ where needed. ⌒ = half step.

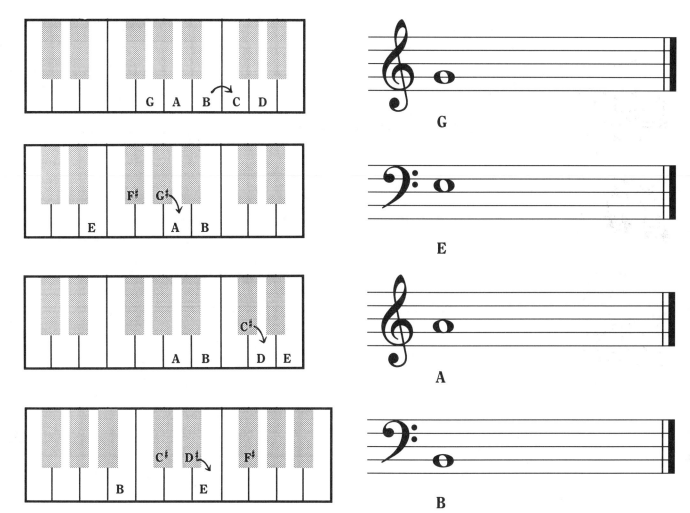

2. Remember the pattern for the pentachord— **W W H W**, use the keyboard picture for reference, and draw the following pentachords.

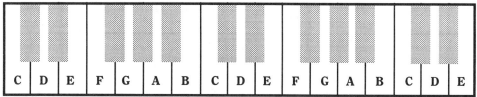

F MAJOR PENTACHORD   C MAJOR PENTACHORD

D MAJOR PENTACHORD   B MAJOR PENTACHORD

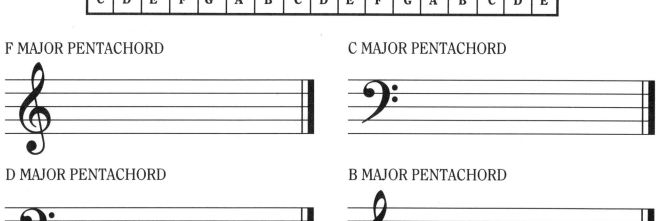

WP351

MAJOR TRIADS

LESSON 12

Look carefully at the C Major **pentachord** below. The term for the three notes written next to the pentachord is a **MAJOR TRIAD.**

C MAJOR PENTACHORD **C MAJOR TRIAD**

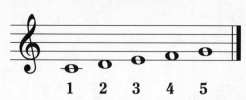 

Discover how to draw **major triads** by answering these questions.

1. The letter names of the 5 notes of the C Major **pentachord** are ___ ___ ___ ___ ___ .

2. The letter names of the 3 notes of the C Major **triad** are ____ ____ ____ .

3. Circle the pattern below that shows what notes of the pentachord = the 3 notes of the triad.

  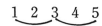 

4. From what you have learned, complete the following **triad rule**:

A **Major triad** is made up of the _____, _____, and _____ notes of the **Major pentachord.**

5. This is the **D Major pentachord and triad**.

The letter names of the 3 notes of the **D major triad** are _____ _____ _____ .

Does the D Major triad contain the correct notes of the pentachord according to **your** rule? _____

6. This is the **B Major pentachord and triad.**

 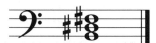

The letter names of the 3 notes of the **B major triad** are _____ _____ _____ .

Does the B Major triad contain the correct notes of the pentachord according to **your** rule? _____

7. Now it is time to put together what you have learned about **pentachords** and **triads** on the keyboard and on the staff. Color the following pentachords with a crayon or colored pencil on the keyboards. Then draw the pentachords and triads on the staffs as shown. The notes of the triad in the example are connected by curved lines. You may want to do this in your examples also.

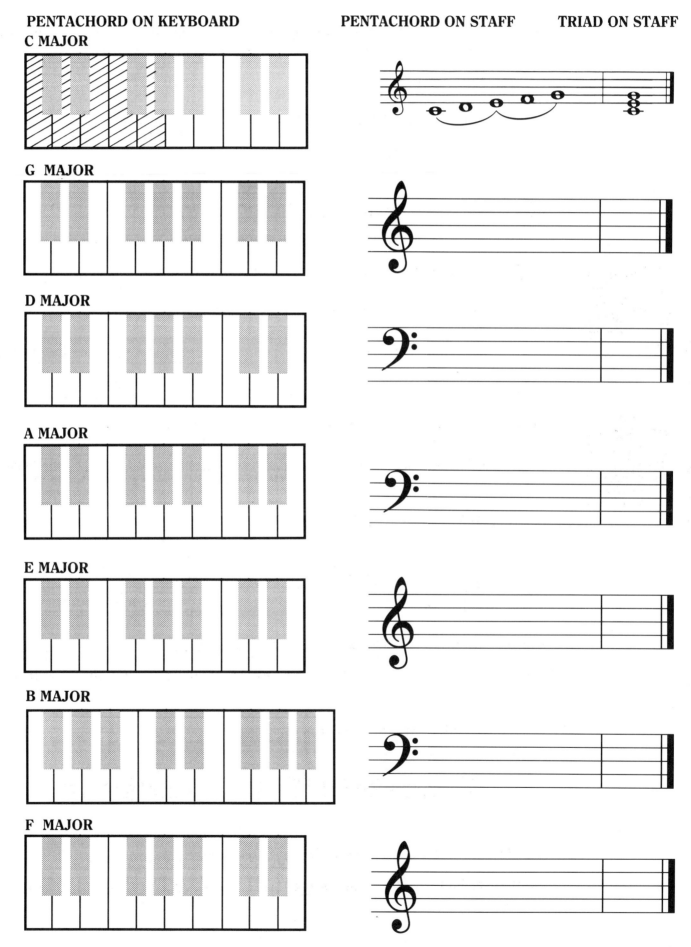

PENTACHORD ON KEYBOARD

C MAJOR

G MAJOR

D MAJOR

A MAJOR

E MAJOR

B MAJOR

F MAJOR

PENTACHORD ON STAFF   TRIAD ON STAFF

LESSON 13 — PENTACHORDS AND TRIADS IN MELODIES

Pentachords and **triads** are often used by composers to **create melodies**.

Listen to the **EXPLORATIONS** tape to hear examples of melodies using pentachords and triads.
As you listen, remember:
- **Pentachords** move by **steps (2nds)**
- **Triads** move by **skips (3rds)**

1. The melodies you hear are based on a **pentachord** or a **triad**. The melodies may move up or down in shape and may be a bit "mixed up." Circle what you hear.

    A. PENTACHORD   TRIAD

    B. PENTACHORD   TRIAD

    C. PENTACHORD   TRIAD

2. The melodies you hear are based on **pentachords**. Listen and look, tracing the melody with your **eye** instead of your pencil. Write the correct letter in the blank.

    Do you hear A or B?

    A.

    B.

    Do you hear C or D? _____

    C.

    D.

3. The melodies you hear are based on **pentachords and triads combined**. Listen and look, tracing the melody shape with your **eye** instead of your pencil. Write the correct letter in the blank.

    Do you hear A or B? _____

    A.

    B.

    Do you hear C or D? _____

    C.
    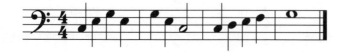

    D.

PRACTICE PAGE

1. Color these **pentachords** on the keyboards.

G MAJOR

D MAJOR

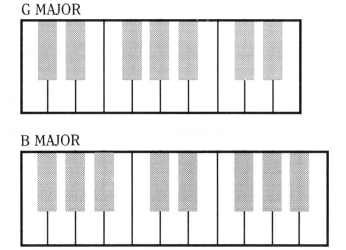
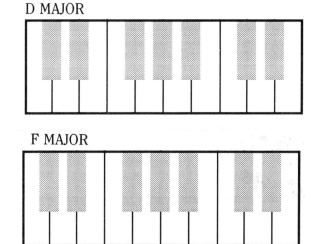

B MAJOR

F MAJOR

2. Write these **pentachords** on the staffs.

C MAJOR

E MAJOR

A MAJOR

F MAJOR

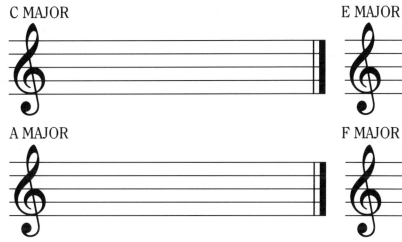

3. Identify these Major **triads** by letter name.

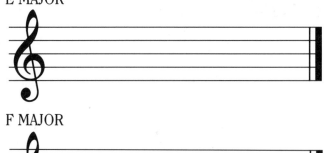
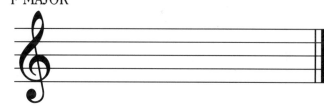

4. Write these **triads** on the staffs.

      D MAJOR   B MAJOR   F MAJOR   C MAJOR   E MAJOR   G MAJOR

5. Identify these Major **pentachords**.

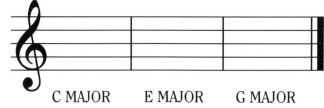

_____   _____   _____   ——WP351

TIE, SLUR, AND PHRASE

LESSON 14

When two notes are connected with a ⌢ and are written on the **SAME** line or space, they are **TIED NOTES**. When playing tied notes, play the first note and **HOLD** through the value of the second note.

TIE

play - hold   play - hold   play - hold

When two notes are connected with a ⌢, and are written on **DIFFERENT** lines or spaces, they are **SLURRED NOTES**. Play slurred notes **LEGATO** (smoothly).

SLUR

When a ⌢ is written under or over a group of notes, it makes a **PHRASE**. All the notes under the ⌢ are played **legato**.

PHRASE

Investigate the musical examples in this book for **tied notes**, **slurred notes**, and **phrases**. Write how many of each you discover.

Musical Example	TIE	SLUR	PHRASE
A Sad Tale, page 26	_____	_____	_____
Playtime, page 33	_____	_____	_____
Galop, page 47	_____	_____	_____

EXPLORE Choose a favorite piece from music you are playing and complete the following:

Title _____ Composer _____

1. How many phrases are in the entire piece? _____

2. How many tied notes are in the piece? _____

3. How many groups of two slurred notes are in the piece? _____

EXPLORE

Carefully look at the opening four measures of **Galop** by **Dmitri Kabalevsky**. Although there are notes you have not yet learned in this book (♫♫ ♫), you should be able to find many things you have learned about as you listen and look at the page.

1. Follow the music on the page as you listen to the example on the **EXPLORATIONS** tape.
It is played on the piano three ways:
  • right hand alone (upper treble clef notes)
  • left hand alone (lower treble clef notes)
  • hands together (all notes)

Galop, op. 39 no. 16 **by Dimitri Kabalevsky**

2. Match the circled items in the music to the list below with the correct letter. Some of the things on the list are **not** in the music so some lines will be left blank.

_____ treble clef	_____ double bar
_____ time signature	_____ pentachord
_____ measure	_____ interval of a 5th
_____ bass clef	_____ interval of a 3rd
_____ sharp	_____ interval of a 2nd
_____ slur	_____ tie

3. By what you have heard and seen in **Galop**, answer the following:

A. Which hand plays **steps** (2nds) most of the time ?   RIGHT   LEFT

B. Which hand plays **skips** (3rds) most of the time?   RIGHT   LEFT

EXPLORE BONUS The bottom staff of **Galop** contains triads that are "broken." Be a musical detective and discover these triads by circling them in the music.

In your words, what is a "broken" triad? 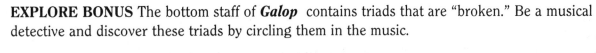_____

PRACTICE PAGE

Use the following pages for writing intervals, pentachords, and triads, and exploring melodies on your instrument!

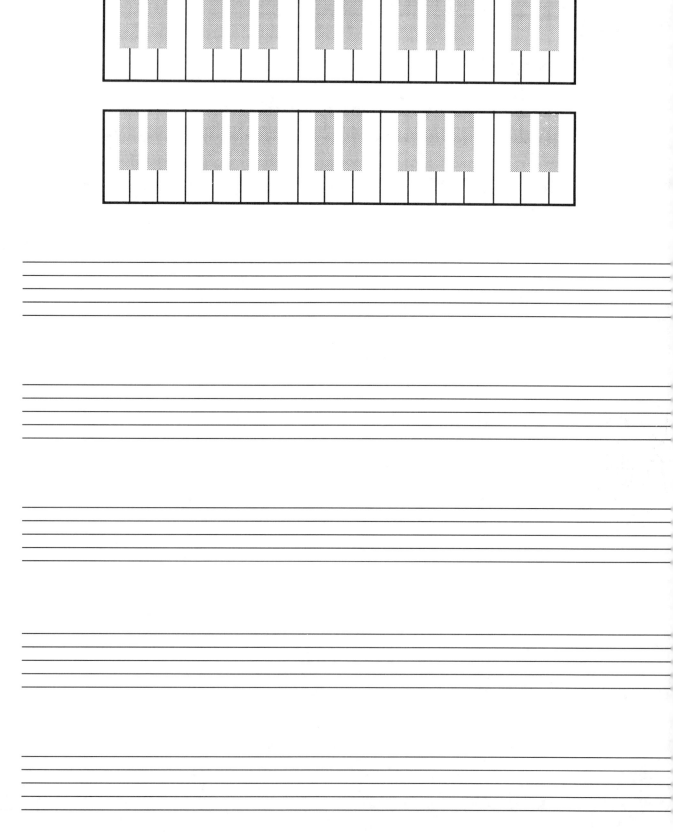

TEST YOUR SKILLS

1. Draw these intervals **above** the notes as harmonies.

_____ *of 8 point*

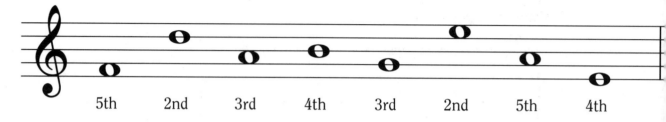

5th   2nd   3rd   4th   3rd   2nd   5th   4th

2. Identify these intervals by writing **2, 3, 4, 5**.

_____ *of 9 point*

_____   _____   _____   _____   _____   _____   _____   _____   _____

3. Draw these **pentachords and triads**.

_____ *of 48 point*

F MAJOR PENTACHORD   TRIAD   G MAJOR PENTACHORD   TRIAD

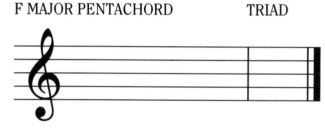
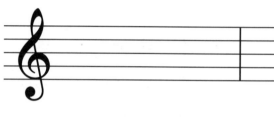

D MAJOR PENTACHORD   TRIAD   A MAJOR PENTACHORD   TRIAD

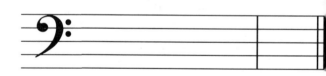

B MAJOR PENTACHORD   TRIAD   E MAJOR PENTACHORD   TRIAD

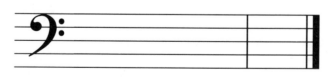

4. Identify these Major pentachords by **letter** name.

_____ *of 4 point*

_____   _____   _____

5. Identify these Major triads by **letter** name. _____ *of 8 points*

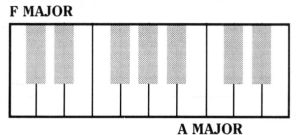   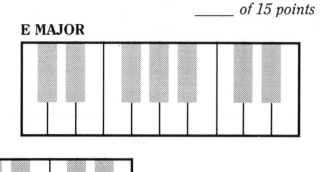

— — — —   — — — —

6. Color these **pentachords** on the keyboards. _____ *of 15 points*

F MAJOR   **E MAJOR**

A MAJOR

7. Match the correct words to the correct notes or symbols. **Circle** the symbols and words that do **not** have a matching partner.

_____ *of 8 points*

A. treble clef _____

B. 3 beats are in each measure _____

C. interval of a 5th _____

D. flat

E. bass clef _____

F. slur _____

G. interval of a 4th _____

H. 4 beats are in each measure _____

I. sharp

J. tie _____

K. natural _____

EXPLORE BONUS Create a melody based on a **D Major pentachord**, with **time signature**, **rhythm**, **bar lines,** and **double bar**. Use the staff paper on page 48, 49, or 63.

_____ *+ 4 points*

UNIT 3
LESSON
15

LOOK AND LISTEN

Draw something in the boxes that will remind you of the sounds of a step and skip.

STEP

SKIP

Many times we are mixed up by the terms **high and low** and **loud and soft.**
Draw something in the boxes **about music** that shows these ideas.

HIGH

LOUD

LOW

SOFT

EXPLORE When we say "Turn the radio up higher," what do we really mean?

_____

_____

1. You have learned about **2nds** and **3rds** as intervals on the staff and have listened to them as **steps** and **skips** in melody shapes. Now listen to these intervals remembering—

   2nds have the sound of a **step**—notes next to each other sound **"close"**
   3rds have the sound of a **skip**—notes that have a note between sound **"open"**

The **EXPLORATIONS** tape has six examples of **steps** and **skips** to identify. Circle your answers.

   A. 2nd (STEP)   3rd (SKIP)   **D.** 2nd (STEP)   3rd (SKIP)

   B. 2nd (STEP)   3rd (SKIP)   **E.** 2nd (STEP)   3rd (SKIP)

   C. 2nd (STEP)   3rd (SKIP)   **F.** 2nd (STEP)   3rd (SKIP)

2. Listen to the **EXPLORATIONS** tape for sounds that move **high** or **low**.

   A. Two notes are played. If the second note is **higher** than the first note, circle **H**. If the second note is **lower** than the first note, circle **L**.

   1. H   L   **4.** H   L

   2. H   L   **5.** H   L

   3. H   L   **6.** H   L

   B. The notes you hear are either **STEPS** or **SKIPS** moving **UP** or **DOWN**. Circle the correct words.

   1. STEPS (2nd)   SKIPS (3rd)   moving   UP   DOWN

   2. STEPS (2nd)   SKIPS (3rd)   moving   UP   DOWN

   3. STEPS (2nd)   SKIPS (3rd)   moving   UP   DOWN

EXPLORE Have fun playing these different types of sounds on your instrument. If you do not play a keyboard instrument, play triads with separate notes ("broken").

   1. A **G Major pentachord** that is **high** on your instrument, played **softly** (p).

   2. An **F Major triad** that is **low** on your instrument, played **loudly** (f).

   3. Three notes moving **down** on your instrument, played **very softly** (pp).

   4. The **highest** and the **lowest** notes on your instrument played pp, p, f, and ff.

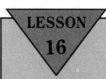

LESSON 16

MUSIC DICTIONARY

Check EXPLORATIONS IN MUSIC, Book 1 page 48 for additional words.

Word	Symbol	Definition	1st Found on Page (You fill in)
ACCIDENTAL	♯ ♭ ♮	Symbol added before a note	39
ALLEGRO		Fast	
ANDANTE		A slow walking speed	
BAR & BRACE	{	Drawn at the start of the grand staff	
CANTABILE		Sweetly singing	
CRESCENDO	◁	Gradually get louder	
DECRESCENDO	▷	Gradually get softer	
DYNAMICS		Musical color	
FLAT	♭	Lowers a note a half step	
FORTE	*f*	Loud	
FORTISSIMO	*ff*	Very loud	
HALF REST	▬	The rest that = two beats in $\frac{2}{4}\ \frac{3}{4}\ \frac{4}{4}\ \frac{5}{4}$	
HALF STEP		A step that has no note between	
HARMONY		Two notes played together	
INTERVAL		The distance between two notes	
LEGATO		Play smoothly	
MEZZO FORTE	*mf*	Medium loud	
MEZZO PIANO	*mp*	Medium soft	
MODERATO		A medium speed	
NATURAL	♮	Cancels a sharp or flat sign	
OSTINATO		A rhythmic or melodic pattern that is repeated	
PENTACHORD	𝄞 ○○○○○	The first 5 notes of a scale	

PHRASE		A group of notes played legato.
PIANO	*p*	Soft
PIANISSIMO	*pp*	Very soft
RITARD., RITARDANDO	*rit.*	Get slower little by little
SHARP	♯	Raises a note a half step
SLUR		Connects two (or more) different notes, to be played legato
STACCATO		Play short and detached
TEMPO		The speed of a composition
TENUTO		Stress and hold
TIE		The first note is played and held through the value of the second note
TRIAD		The 1st, 3rd, and 5th notes of a scale
WHOLE REST	—	The rest that = 4 beats in $\frac{2}{4}\frac{3}{4}\frac{4}{4}\frac{5}{4}$
WHOLE STEP		A step that has a note in the middle of the step

USING MUSIC TERMS

1. The **tempo** of a piece is written at the beginning of the music in **Italian**, and describes how fast or slow you should perform the music. Draw something in each box to show the tempo described. It does **not** have to be something musical.

ALLEGRO	**MODERATO**	**ANDANTE**

2. Write the music terms that are **opposites** of these words.

fortissimo _____   crescendo _____

staccato _____   piano _____

WP351

BEYOND THE PAGE

You can now investigate the music you are learning for all of the things you have learned in this book. Choose a piece you enjoy and discover the following details.

Music Investigation Report

Title_____

Composer _____**Date of report**_____

1. The **time signature** of the piece is ☐

2. Copy the **notes and rests** from the first measure of the piece. Remember to include the clef(s) and time signature.

_____
_____
_____
_____
_____

_____
_____
_____
_____
_____

3. Write the **letter** name under each note in the measure above.

4. Look through the entire piece for **triads**. How many did you discover? _____

5. Look through the entire piece for **pentachords**. How many did you discover? _____

6. Ask your teacher if you may circle three examples of the intervals you have learned. Find examples of **2nds, 3rds, 4ths, and 5ths**. Label each in pencil. Remember that intervals can be written as **harmonies** or as **melodies**.

7. The composer may have chosen a **tempo,** or speed, for the piece. Look above the staff at the beginning. Copy the words you see: _____. Use a music dictionary if you do not know the words.

8. Investigate the music for the composer's directions about how the piece should be played with **dynamics.** Look for a page that has an interesting dynamic **"color path"** and draw it. The dynamic color path for page _____ is:

Congratulations! You have been a Musical Detective in your own music!

PRACTICE PAGE

Use this page for overall drill of **Units 1, 2,** and **3** to prepare for the **Final Test**.

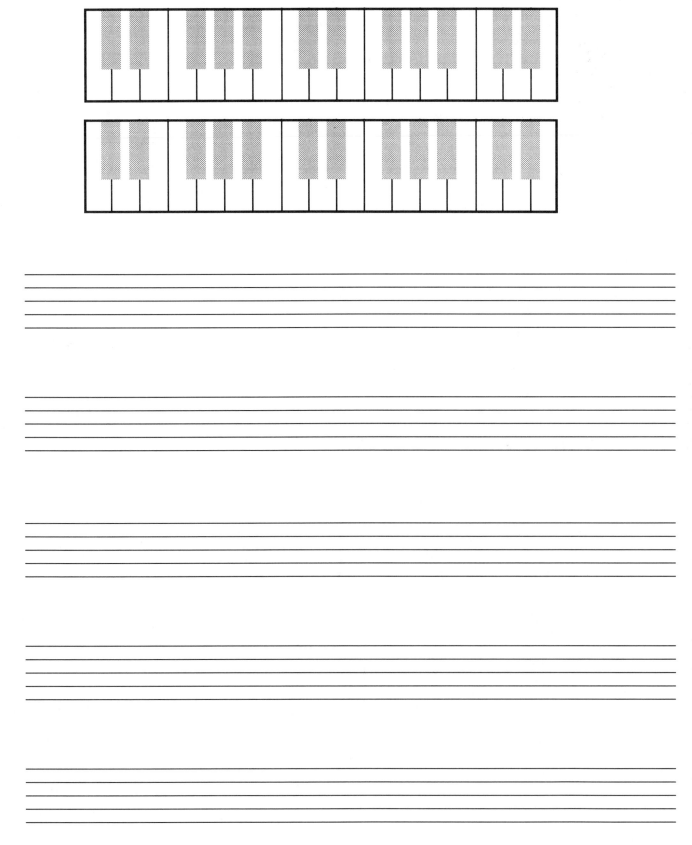

_____ *Your Score*

TEST YOUR SKILLS

1. Write the **letter names** of the notes. _____ *of 12 points*

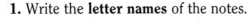
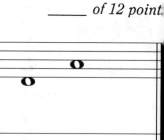

2. Put **bar lines** in the correct places in the following examples. **Write the counts** under each measure. End each example with a double bar.

A. _____ *of 8 points*

Counts:_____

B.

Counts:_____

3. Complete each measure with one **note. Write the counts** below each measure. _____ *of 7 points*

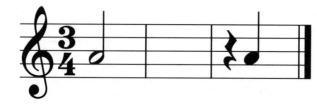
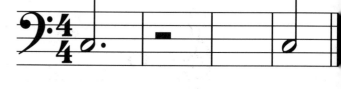

4. Match the terms to the correct symbols. **Circle** the words and symbols that do not have partners.

A. quarter note _____ *of 10 points*

B. whole rest

C. crescendo

D. whole step

E. staccato

F. half rest

G. decrescendo

H. half step

I. half note

5. Draw the following Major **pentachords and triads**. _____ *of 10 points*

C MAJOR PENTACHORD   TRIAD   F MAJOR PENTACHORD   TRIAD

D MAJOR PENTACHORD   TRIAD   G MAJOR PENTACHORD   TRIAD

6. Draw a **grand staff** with correct bar and brace, clefs, bar lines to show measures, and a double bar.

_____ *of 6 points*

7. Identify the intervals by **number**. _____ *of 8 points*

____   ____   ____   ____   ____   ____   ____   ____

8. Write the intervals **above** the notes as harmonies. _____ *of 8 points*

3rd   2nd   5th   4th   3rd   5th   2nd   4th

9. Match the words to the correct definitions. _____ *of 6 points*

A. legato   _____ fast

B. piano   _____ a medium speed

C. andante   _____ play smoothly

D. allegro   _____ get slower little by little

E. ritard   _____ soft

F. moderato   _____ a slow walking speed

WP351

10. Find the following items in the music example. Write the correct letter names in the boxes. Some boxes will be empty when you are finished!

_____ of 6 point

A. tied notes   D. sharp
B. bar line   E. dotted half note
C. time signature   F. half rest

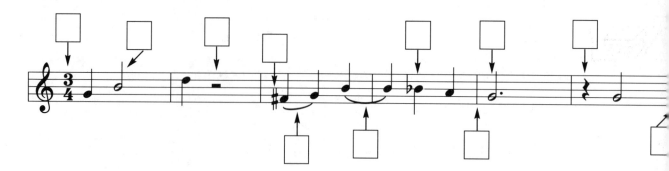

BONUS Write two rhythm examples. **Write the counts** below each measure.   _____ + 4 points

EXPLORE BONUS Compose a four-measure piece using—   _____ + 6 points
   1. pentachord in G Major
   2. triad in G Major
   3. at least one half note
   4. time signature
   5. at least one quarter rest
   6. slurred notes

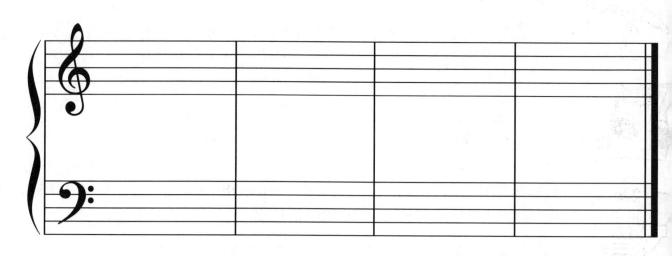

11. Listen to the **EXPLORATIONS** tape! _____ *of 6 points*

A. Is the second note you hear **higher** or **lower** than the first? Circle H or L.

1. H   L   4. H   L

2. H   L   5. H   L

3. H   L   6. H   L

B. Do the notes move by **steps** or **skips**? Circle your answers. _____ *of 6 points*

1. STEP (2nd)   SKIP (3rd)   4. STEP (2nd)   SKIP (3rd)

2. STEP (2nd)   SKIP (3rd)   5. STEP (2nd)   SKIP (3rd)

3. STEP (2nd)   SKIP (3rd)   6. STEP (2nd)   SKIP (3rd)

C. The music you hear is in either **2/4** , **3/4** , or **4/4** . Circle your answers. _____ *of 4 points*

1. 2/4 3/4 4/4   3. 2/4 3/4 4/4

2. 2/4 3/4 4/4   4. 2/4 3/4 4/4

D. Listen to each rhythm. Decide if it is the same or different from the one written. Circle your answers. _____ *of 3 points*

1. [rhythm notation]   SAME   DIFFERENT

2. [rhythm notation]   SAME   DIFFERENT

3. [rhythm notation]   SAME   DIFFERENT

EXPLORE BONUS _____ *+ 4 points*

1. Rhythm: Listen to the rhythm on the **EXPLORATIONS** tape and try to **write what you hear**. The rhythm is played two times. The time signature and first note are written.

2. Melody: Listen to the melody on the tape. It uses the same rhythm as above and moves by **steps**. Try to **write** it. The first and last notes are written.

CONGRATULATIONS for learning so much. Turn the page if you want to listen and explore more!

WP351

EXTEND YOUR LISTENING

If you enjoyed the **EXPLORE BONUS** examples in **TEST YOUR SKILLS**, you may like to try a few more listening examples of **writing what you hear.**

Listen to the rhythm examples on the **EXPLORATIONS** tape. They are played two times. **Write what you hear**. The first note is written.

1.

$\frac{4}{4}$

2.

$\frac{3}{4}$

3.

$\frac{4}{4}$

Listen to the melodies. They are played two times. They are based on the rhythms above. **Write what you hear**. The first and last notes are written.

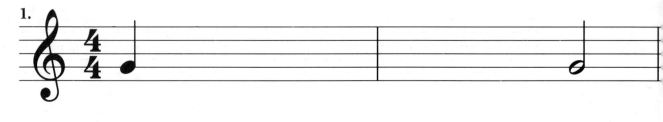

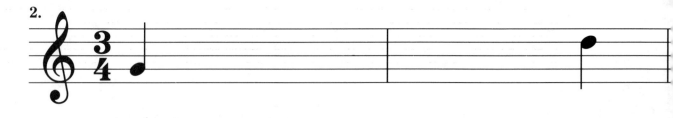

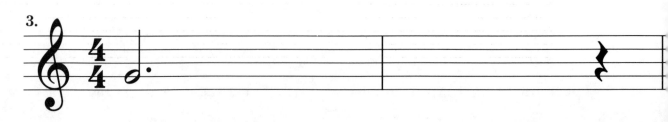

EXPLORE AND EXCEL

Use this page to explore a new **music story** or write a **rhythm exercise** or **compose** a melody. It's your choice!

ANSWERS FOR LISTENING EXAMPLES

pages 24 & 25
L4
3. 1. B
   2. C
   3. F
   5. A. $\frac{3}{4}$ B. $\frac{2}{4}$ C. $\frac{4}{4}$ D. $\frac{3}{4}$

page 35
L7
5. 1. A
   2. C
   3. F

page 44
L8
1. A. TRIAD
   B. PENTACHORD
   C. PENTACHORD

2. 1. B
   2. C

3. 1. A
   2. C

page 53
L10
1. A. 2nd   D. 3rd
   B. 3rd   E. 3rd
   C. 2nd   F. 2nd

2. A. 1. H   4. H
      2. L   5. L
      3. L   6. H

   B. 1. Steps moving Up
      2. Skips moving Down
      3. Steps moving Down

page 61
L11
11. A. 1. H   4. H
       2. H   5. L
       3. L   6. L

    B. 1. Step   4. Step
       2. Skip   5. Step
       3. Skip   6. Skip

    C. 1. $\frac{3}{4}$ 2. $\frac{2}{4}$ 3. $\frac{3}{4}$ 4. $\frac{4}{4}$

    D. 1. DIFFERENT
       2. SAME
       3. DIFFERENT

page 61
L12
EXPLORE BONUS
1. Rhythm:

2. Melody:

page 62
L13
Rhythms: 1.

2.

3.

Melodies: 1.

2.

3.